Teri Sherman

Gothic Halloween

A Scary Adult Coloring Book

Blue Star Coloring Books is in San Antonio, TX and Portland, OR.

Teamwork makes the dream work: This book was illustrated by Teri, designed by Peter, written by Gabe and published by CJ. Adult Coloring Book, Stress Relieving Patterns and Blue Star are trademarks of PCG Publishing Group, LLC. The copyright © belongs to Blue Star as of 2016. We reserve all of our rights.

Printed in the United States of America.

We Love What You Create

And We Want to Shout It From the Rooftops

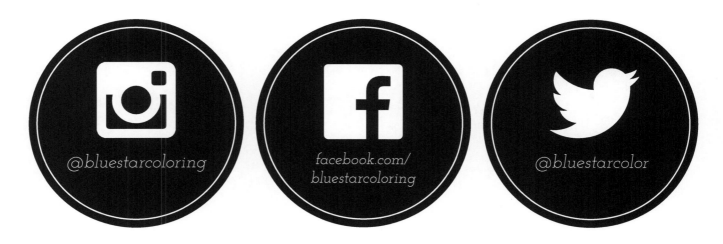

@bluestarcoloring

facebook.com/
bluestarcoloring

@bluestarcolor

#bluestarcoloring

bluestarcoloring.com

Show Us
Your Art

We'll Show
The World

We'll never be perfect, but that won't stop us from trying. Your feedback makes us a better company. We want your ideas, criticism, compliments or anything else you think we should hear!

Oh, and if you don't love this coloring book, we'll refund your money immediately. No questions asked.

Send anything and everything to contact@bluestarcoloring.com

How to Use This Book

 Break out your crayons or colored pencils.

 Turn off your phone, tablet, computer, whatever.

 Find your favorite page in the book. That is the beginning.

 Start coloring.

 If you notice at any point that you have goosebumps, chills or that your pulse is pounding, take a deep breath and let the world hear your loudest, most blood-curdling scream. Remind yourself that coloring is usually stress-relieving, but during Halloween, it can be downright terrifying.

 When you don't feel like it anymore, stop. After coloring, avoid exposure to direct sunlight for a period of time lasting – well, pretty much forever. (You might consider investing in a nice comfortable coffin to sleep in during the day.)

About the Artist

A lifelong artist, Teri Sherman has illustrated, crafted and colored countless projects throughout her career. Now residing and creating in the tiny Scottish village of Fochabers (no, that's not a curse word,) she uses her "crafty hands" to create art with a darker side. Her first coloring grimoire, Gothic Halloween, was published in October 2015 by Blue Star Coloring.

Connect with Teri!

https://www.etsy.com/uk/shop/ArtiDoodles

Just a reminder: Teri is an independent artist, meaning that her opinions and artistic expressions are hers, and not necessarily ours.

READY FOR THE NEXT ONE?

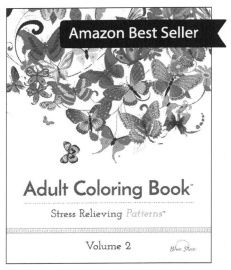
Adult Coloring Book
Stress Relieving *Patterns*
Volume 2
Blue Star

Adult Coloring Book
Stress Relieving *Animal Designs*
Blue Star

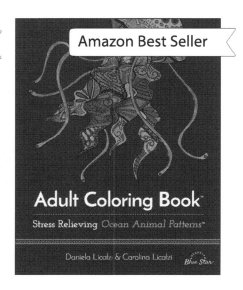
Adult Coloring Book
Stress Relieving *Ocean Animal Patterns*
Daniela Licalzi & Carolina Licalzi   Blue Star

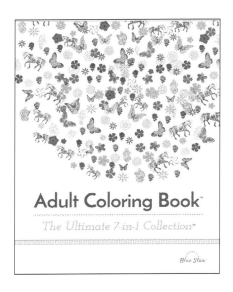
Adult Coloring Book
The Ultimate 7-in-1 Collection
Blue Star

Soul of the Woodland
A Stress Relieving *Adult Coloring Book*
Suzy Joyner   Blue Star

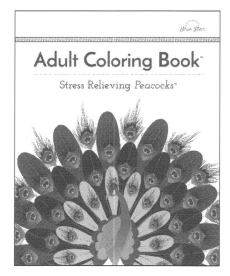
Adult Coloring Book
Stress Relieving *Peacocks*

Dia de los Muertos
Day of the Dead & Sugar Skull Coloring Book
Blue Star

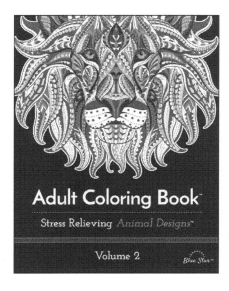
Adult Coloring Book
Stress Relieving *Animal Designs*
Volume 2   Blue Star

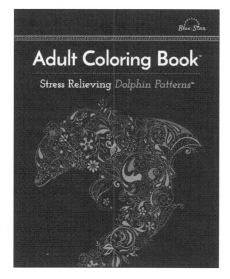
Adult Coloring Book
Stress Relieving *Dolphin Patterns*

Color the Cosmos™
A Stress Relieving *Adult Coloring Book*™

Daniela Licalzi & Carolina Licalzi · Blue Star

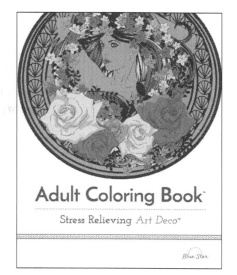

Adult Coloring Book™
Stress Relieving *Art Deco*™

Blue Star

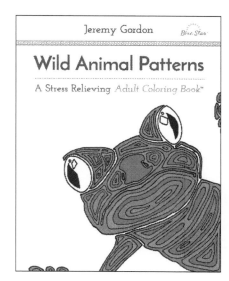

Jeremy Gordon · Blue Star

Wild Animal Patterns
A Stress Relieving *Adult Coloring Book*™

Adult Coloring Book™
Stress Relieving *Cats*™

Blue Star

Coloring Book for Adults
Stress Relieving *Stained Glass Patterns*™

Blue Star

Mom & Daughter
Coloring Book

Blue Star

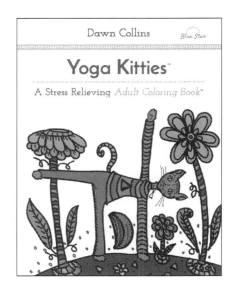

Dawn Collins · Blue Star

Yoga Kitties™
A Stress Relieving *Adult Coloring Book*™

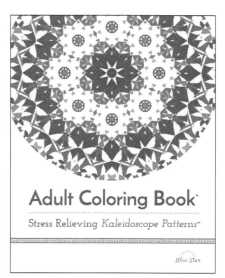

Adult Coloring Book™
Stress Relieving *Kaleidoscope Patterns*™

Blue Star

Adult Coloring Book™
Stress Relieving *Paisley Patterns*™

Blue Star

Look for the *Blue Star*™

bluestarcoloring.com

Printed in Great Britain
by Amazon